National Curriculum
Key Stage 3 Age 13–14

Practice Papers

Key Stage 3 National Tests

MATHS

How the Key Stage 3 National Tests will affect your education

● All students in Year 9 (age 13–14) will take National Tests in English, Mathematics and Science. These important tests are held in May each year and are designed to be an objective assessment of the work you will have done during Key Stage 3 (Years 7–9) of the National Curriculum.

● You will also have your school work assessed by your teachers. These teacher assessments will be set alongside your results in the National Tests to give a clear picture of your overall achievement.

● In July, the test results together with the teacher assessments will be reported to parents/guardians.

● The results may be used by your teacher to help place you in the appropriate teaching group for some GCSE courses next year.

How this book will help your education

● This book offers plenty of practice in the type of question you will face in the Key Stage 3 National Test for Mathematics, including Mental Mathematics.

● The answers and a mark scheme have been provided to allow you to check how you have done.

● The 'Examiner's tip' boxes in the Answers section give you advice on how to improve your answers and avoid common mistakes.

● A unique Marking grid allows you to record your results and estimate the level of the National Curriculum at which you are working.

The test questions, answers and 'Examiner's tips' contained in this publication are based upon the official test materials provided to schools, but do not reproduce those tests exactly. The official tests are supported by administrative and other guidance for teachers to use in setting the tests, marking them and interpreting their results. The results you achieve in taking the tests in this book may not be the same as you achieve in the official tests.

Every effort has been made to trace copyright holders and to obtain their permission for the use of copyright material. The authors and publishers will gladly receive any information enabling them to rectify any error or omission in subsequent editions.

First published 1996
Reprinted 1996
Revised 1997, 1998, 1999, 2000, 2001, 2002, 2003

Text: © Mark Patmore and Brian Seager 2001, 2002
Design and illustrations: © Letts Educational Ltd 2001, 2002

Series editor: Bob McDuell

British Library Cataloguing in Publication Data
A CIP record for this book is available from the British Library

ISBN 1 84315 063 8

Cover design by 2idesign, Cambridge
Cover logo by Starfish Design for Print, London
Project management and typesetting by Hardlines Ltd, Charlbury, Oxford

Printed in Italy

Letts Educational Ltd
The Chiswick Centre
414 Chiswick High Road
London
W4 5TF
Telephone: 020 8996 3333
Fax: 020 8742 8390
email: mail@lettsed.co.uk
website: www.letts-education.com

Letts Educational Limited is a division of Granada Learning Limited, part of Granada plc.

Contents

What you need to know about the National Tests 4

Preparing and practising for the Maths Test 6

National Curriculum requirements 9

Instructions 11

Test A (Levels 4–6) (without calculator) 12

Test B (Levels 4–6) (calculator can be used) 22

Test C (Levels 5–7) (without calculator) 32

Test D (Levels 5–7) (calculator can be used) 40

Test E (Levels 6–8) (without calculator) 49

Mental Mathematics Test 1: Answer sheet 57

Mental Mathematics Test 2: Answer sheet 58

Mental Mathematics Test 1: Questions 59

Mental Mathematics Test 2: Questions 60

Answers 61

Determining your level 78

Marking grid 79

What you need to know about the National Tests

What is the purpose of National Tests?

The tests, taken by students in Year 9, have several functions:

- they provide the government with a snapshot picture of attainment throughout the country, enabling it to make judgements about whether standards are improving nationally;
- they give information to OFSTED about schools achievements, so that they can judge which schools are improving and which are deemed to be failing their students;
- they give you information about your progress compared to national standards;
- they may be used by teachers to place you in the appropriate teaching group for the GCSE courses starting in Year 10.

How do the tests work?

In May of Year 9, you will take tests on the core subjects of English, Mathematics and Science. In Maths the written tests are grouped into four ranges of levels called 'tiers'. The four tiers cover levels 3–5, 4–6, 5–7 and 6–8. Each tier has two written test papers, the first of which must be completed without the use of a calculator, together with a Mental Mathematics test. The tests are not marked in school by a teacher, but posted off to an external marker, who is often a teacher in another school or a retired teacher. External markers have been trained in marking the tests so that all students' test papers throughout the country are marked to the same standard.

Once the tests have been marked, the mark is translated into a 'level'. The level that each mark corresponds to is decided according to results gained in pre-tests and the tests themselves. It varies slightly from year to year. The test papers, marks and levels are returned to your school in July. The levels are then reported to your parents/guardians.

What do the tests assess?

The tests are designed to assess your knowledge, skills and understanding in the context of the programme of study set out in the National Curriculum. This can be found on the National Curriculum website, www.nc.uk.net. The programme of study is divided into four sections, called Attainment Targets:

- Ma1 – Using and applying Mathematics
- Ma2 – Number and algebra
- Ma3 – Shape, space and measures
- Ma4 – Handling data

Questions in the tests cover all four Attainment Targets, but the questions assessing Ma1 are usually set within the context of one of the other Attainment Targets.

What are the levels and what do they mean?

There is a set of benchmark standards that measure a student's progress through the first three Key Stages of the National Curriculum. Attainment is measured in steps called 'levels', from 1 to 8. The National Curriculum document sets out the knowledge, skills and understanding that students should demonstrate at each level. The government target is for students to achieve level 2 at the end of Key Stage 1, level 4 at the end of Key Stage 2 and level 5 or 6 at the end of Key Stage 3. The chart below shows these government targets.

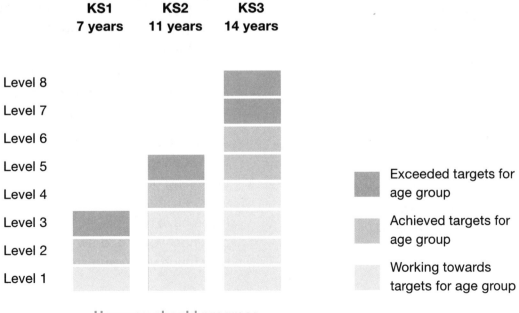

How you should progress

Preparing and practising for the Maths Test

The questions in this book test the same things as the actual test papers:

- knowledge
- understanding
- handling information
- interpretation and evaluation
- solving problems.

What are the key features of this book?

This book contains all you need to prepare for the tests:

- National Curriculum requirements – key information for each of the Attainment Targets Ma1, Ma2, Ma3 and Ma4.
- Questions – one non-calculator and one calculator practice test paper for both levels 4–6 and levels 5–7, a non-calculator paper for levels 6–8 and two Mental Mathematics papers. This means that you will find plenty of questions to practise, regardless of which tier you are entered for.
- Answers – showing the responses that will gain credit in the tests and how the marks are allocated.
- Examiner's tips – advice on how to improve your performance.
- Level charts – what the marks mean in terms of National Curriculum levels.

How should I use this book?

Try taking Tests A and B first, on different days. Mark each test to see how you have done. If your results indicate that you are working at Level 5 or higher, then you should try Tests C and D, which are more challenging, some time later. Work through the answers and advice to see where you might have done better on Tests A and B. When you've had a chance to improve your understanding, take Tests C and D on different days. The **Letts Key Stage 3 Success** range shown on the back cover is our recommended revision source.

First, make sure that you have:

- read the instructions on page 11;
- all the equipment on page 8;
- revised all the commonly used formulae, e.g. for a circle $C = 2\pi r$, $A = \pi r^2$, and Pythagoras' theorem $a^2 + b^2 = c^2$. The only formulae you will be given are listed for you on page 8 and may be referred to during the written tests but **not** during the mental tests.
- a quiet room in which to work, where you will be comfortable and will not be disturbed.

Allow one hour to take each test. Note your starting time in the box at the beginning of the test and time yourself; stop writing after 60 minutes. If you have not finished but wish to continue working, draw a line to show how much you completed within the test time, then continue for as long as you wish. You are allowed to ask an adult to explain the meaning of words you do not understand, provided that they are not mathematical terms such as 'quadrilateral'. Some questions set in the National Tests now require you show that you are 'Using and applying Mathematics' (Attainment Target Ma1). These questions are indicated with a diamond (◆).

After completing the test, work through the paper along with the answers and advice at the back of the book. It is a good idea to highlight or make a note of areas where you do not do well, so that you can revise these at a later stage. Record your marks in the top half of the boxes in the margin. You will also see subtotal boxes at the bottom of each section of the test – you can keep a running total there. If you required extra time to complete the test, do not count the marks for the 'extra' questions in your final score.

Work out the total marks gained for each question, write them in the grid on page 79 and add them up to get the total mark for the paper. Then use the charts on page 78 to determine the level of your performance on each test as well as an overall level.

Mental Mathematics is an important part of the National Curriculum and there is a separate Mental Mathematics Test in addition to the two written papers.

The test assesses your mental recall and ability to deal with numerical problems, and it counts for 20% of the final mark.

Two Mental Mathematics Tests are included on pages 59 and 60 of this book. You should detach these pages and get someone to read out each question twice to you. You will then have 5, 10 or 15 seconds to complete your answer, which should be written on the answer sheets (pages 57–58).

If you achieve at least level 6 in Tests A–D, you should try Test E, which is intended to assess levels 6–8. This test should also take 60 minutes. Again, total your marks on the Marking grid and work out your level using the chart on page 78.

What does the level mean?

The tests in this book give a guide as to the level that you are likely to achieve in the actual tests. We hope that, through practice, these tests will give you the confidence to achieve your best. By working through the answers and notes, you should be able to improve your achievement.

How do I prepare to take the actual tests?

A few days before the test:

- work through some practice questions, making sure that you understand which answers are correct and why;

- check that you know which test papers you will be taking and when these are to be sat;

- double check that you have all the necessary equipment.

Above all, don't worry too much! Although the National Tests are important, your achievement throughout the school year is equally important. Do your best in these tests; that is all that anyone can ask.

Equipment you will need

The following equipment may be needed for answering these questions:

- a pen, pencil and rubber;

- a ruler (a 30 cm plastic ruler is most suitable);

- a calculator (an inexpensive four-function calculator is all that is required. Do not use a scientific calculator that has too many complicated functions);

- an angle measurer (this is probably easier to use than a protractor, particularly for angles greater than 180°).

- tracing paper (this is useful for rotational symmetry questions);

- a pair of compasses (use this for drawing circles);

- a mirror (this is useful for symmetry questions).

Formulae you will need

Area of a trapezium

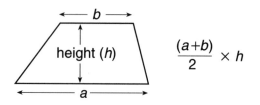

$$\frac{(a+b)}{2} \times h$$

Volume of a prism

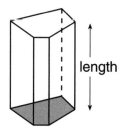

area of cross section × length

National Curriculum requirements

Ma1 Using and applying Mathematics: Requirements at each level

Level 4 Develop strategies for solving problems; apply mathematics to practical situations. Present information and results in a clear and organised way.

Level 5 Identify and obtain information needed to solve problems. Check whether results are sensible. Describe situations mathematically, using symbols, words and diagrams. Draw conclusions and explain reasoning.

Level 6 Solve complex problems by breaking them down. Interpret information in a variety of forms. Explain use of diagrams and give mathematical justifications.

Level 7 Refine and extend the mathematics used to give fuller solutions. Explain and give reasons for form of presentation used. Justify generalisations, arguments and solutions.

Level 8 Follow alternative approaches and use a range of mathematical techniques. Use symbols precisely and consistently. Comment constructively on reasoning and results.

Gifted and Talented Indicates exceptional performance at level 8.

Ma2 Number and algebra: Requirements at each level

Level 4 Understand place value; multiply and divide whole numbers by 10 and 100. Use mental recall of multiplication facts up to 10 × 10. Use efficient written methods of addition, subtraction, multiplication and division. Add, subtract and order decimals. Check answers for reasonableness. Use simple fractions and percentages. Recognise and describe number patterns and use formulae in words. Use simple coordinates.

Level 5 Multiply and divide by 10, 100 and 1000. Add, subtract and order negative numbers and work with decimals. Simplify fractions and solve problems involving ratio and proportion. Calculate fractional and percentage parts, with and without a calculator. Use non-calculator methods to multiply and divide. Check solutions by reversing the operation or approximating. Use simple formulae and brackets. Use and interpret coordinates.

Level 6 Order and approximate decimals. Solve problems involving comparisons, giving one number as a fraction or percentage of another. Use equivalence between fractions, decimals and percentages and work with ratios. Add and subtract fractions. Find rules for number sequences and solve linear equations. Draw graphs on coordinate diagrams.

Level 7 Use one significant figure estimates. Use a calculator efficiently and appropriately. Calculate proportional changes. Use algebra and graphical methods to solve simultaneous equations. Solve simple inequalities.

Level 8 Calculate with powers, roots and numbers in standard form. Solve problems involving repeated proportional change. Evaluate and manipulate algebraic formulae and expressions; find common factors; multiply out brackets. Solve inequalities and interpret graphs, including those that model real life situations.

Gifted and Talented Indicates exceptional performance at level 8.

Ma3 Shape, space and measures: Requirements at each level

Level 4 Draw 2-D shapes on grids. Reflect shapes in mirror lines. Read a variety of scales. Find simple perimeters and areas.

Level 5 Measure and draw angles to nearest degree. Know the angle sums in a triangle and at a point. Identify symmetries. Know rough metric equivalents of imperial units still in use and convert between metric units. Make sensible estimations in everyday situations. Use formula for area of a triangle.

Level 6 Use 2-D representations of 3-D objects. Classify quadrilaterals and solve problems involving angle and symmetry properties of polygons, intersecting and parallel lines and explain these. Find circumference and area of circles, areas of plane figures and volume of cuboids. Draw enlargements of shapes.

Level 7 Use Pythagoras' theorem. Calculate lengths, areas and volumes in plane shapes and prisms. Find the locus of an object according to a rule. Understand error in measurement and use compound measures.

Level 8 Use congruence and similarity and sine, cosine and tangent in right-angled triangles when solving problems.

Gifted and Talented Indicates exceptional performance at level 8.

Ma4 Handling data: Requirements at each level

Level 4 Collect and record data using a frequency table. Use mode and range. Group data and represent these in frequency diagrams. Interpret frequency diagrams and simple line graphs.

Level 5 Find mean of discrete data and compare two distributions, using range, mode, median or mean. Interpret graphs and diagrams and draw conclusions. Use probability scale from 0 to 1 and find probabilities based on equally likely outcomes or experimental evidence.

Level 6 Collect and record continuous data and create grouped frequency tables. Construct frequency diagrams and pie charts. Understand correlation and draw conclusions from scatter diagrams. Identify all the outcomes of combined experiments and represent these. Use the fact that the total probability of all the mutually exclusive outcomes of an experiment is 1.

Level 7 Find the modal class and estimate the mean, median and range of sets of grouped data. Compare distributions and make inferences based on measures of average and range. Draw a line of best fit on a scatter diagram. Use relative frequency as an estimate of probability.

Level 8 Use cumulative frequency tables and diagrams to estimate median and interquartile range; compare and make inferences. Calculate the probability of a compound event.

Gifted and Talented Indicates exceptional performance at level 8.

Instructions

Each test should take 60 minutes. Enter your start and finish times in the boxes at the beginning of each test.

Try to answer all of the questions.

Read the questions carefully. If you think, after reading a question carefully, that you cannot answer it, leave it and come back to it later.

The questions you have to answer are given in blue boxes. For example:

How many 3 litre cans does Asif have to buy to cover an area of 254 square metres?

Write your answers and working on the test papers in this book.

The ✏ shows where you should answer the question. The lines or space given should give you some indication of what is expected.

Look at the number of marks for each part of a question. This is shown in a box in the margin, for example:

1
Q1a

There is also a box showing the maximum number of marks for each section. You can write in your subtotal, so that you can see at a glance how you are doing.

In Mathematics, marks are awarded for the method you use as well as the answer. It is important to show your working clearly so you can receive credit.

You must not use a calculator in Tests A, C or E, but a calculator may be used in Tests B and D.

Look carefully at the words you write, particularly mathematical words. Read your answers carefully to yourself and make sure you have clearly expressed what you mean.

GOOD LUCK!

Test A
Levels 4–6

START

FINISH

WITHOUT CALCULATOR

1 Below is a list of mathematical words.

Use suitable words from this list to complete the sentences below.

cube factor integer multiple square square root sum

1
Q1a

1
Q1b

1
Q1c

4
Q2

 a 45 is a .... of 5.

b 49 is the .... of 7.

c 3 is a .... of 81.

2 Here are some wall tiles.
Draw in all the lines of symmetry.

a
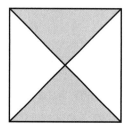

b
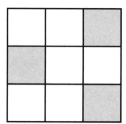

c
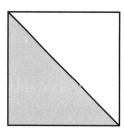

d
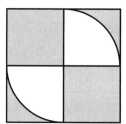

3   Show the probabilities of these events on the probability line.

Mark each with an arrow and its letter.

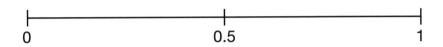

0   0.5   1

a If I throw an ordinary dice, the number will be odd.

b If I throw an ordinary dice, I shall get a 6.

c It will snow in London on 1st August next year.

d The next king will be a man.

1
Q3a

1
Q3b

1
Q3c

1
Q3d

4   Below are various shapes.

Identify the shape that is similar to the shaded shape, and the shape that is congruent to the shaded shape.

◆   2
Q4

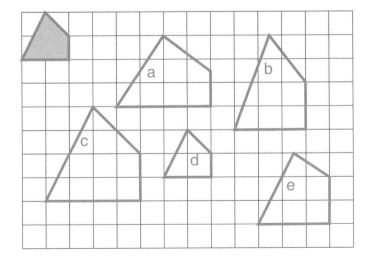

Shape .... is similar.

Shape .... is congruent.

5 Chuck is an American visiting France.
He needs a new shirt.

This formula shows you how to work out the French sizes for given American sizes.

> French size is twice
> the American size
> plus 9.

a Find the French size for American size 17.

....

b Write a formula for the French size (F) in terms of the American size (A).

....

c Chuck bought a French size 37.
What is the American size?

....

6 Look at the equations below.
Fill in the missing numbers.

a $43 \times 10 =$ ....

b $6200 \div 100 =$ ....

c .... × 100 = 7000

d 21 000 ÷ .... = 210

e 830 × .... = 830 000

f 940 ÷ 100 = ...

g 0.026 × .... = 2.6

h .... ÷ 1000 = 0.38

7 Eric measured his desk. It was 65 cm deep and 1 metre 7 cm wide.

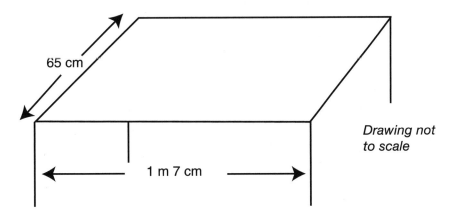

65 cm

1 m 7 cm

Drawing not to scale

a Write the measurements in

   (i) millimetres ....

   (ii) metres ....

b Roughly, how many feet are these measurements?

....

8
Q6

2
Q7a

2
Q7b

Max. 15
Qs 5–7
subtotal

15

8 Here are the results of tests on two brands of torch battery.
Which would you buy? Give a reason.

	Mean	Range
Brand A	15 hours	3.5 hours
Brand B	14 hours	1.7 hours

....

....

9 Bob is having a barbecue with his friends.
He wants to buy 45 tins of baked beans at 17p a tin.

a How much would this cost?

....

b The shopkeeper gives him a 20% discount. How much does he pay?

....

10 a Look at the expression below.
Simplify it.

$2c + 3d - c + 4d$

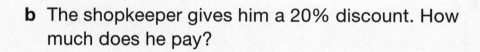

....

b What must you add to $3x + 2y$ to get $5x - 2y$?

....

1
Q10b

c Find the value of $5x - 2y$ when $x = 3$ and $y = -4$.

....

2
Q10c

d Solve these equations.

(i) $\dfrac{x}{3} = 10$

....

1
Q10d(i)

(ii) $3x + 10 = 7$

....

2
Q10d(ii)

11 Here are 5 number cards.

| 2 | 4 | 5 | 5 | 8 |

Use all the cards to make an addition sum that has the answer 600.

2
Q11

```
  ☐ ☐ ☐
+   ☐ ☐
─────────
  6 0 0
```

Max. 15
Qs 8–11
subtotal

12 Gill has three spinners to use in a game.
Here is the first. It is unbiased.

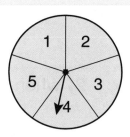

a The arrow is spun once.

(i) What is the probability that it lands on 4?

1
Q12a(i)

....

(ii) What is the probability that it lands on an odd number?

1
Q12a(ii)

....

b The second spinner is biased.
Here are the results of 10 spins.

Result	1	2	3	4	5
Number of times	1	2	1	1	5

(i) Explain why the probability of getting a 2 need not be 0.2.

1
Q12b(i)

....

....

Here are the results of 100 spins.

Result	1	2	3	4	5
Number of times	10	23	21	16	30

(ii) What is the probability that on the next spin the arrow will land on 2?

1

Q12b(ii)

....

c The third spinner also has five numbers.
Here are some of the probabilities.

Result	1	2	3	4	5
Probability	0.1	0.3	0.1		0.25

(i) What is the probability of the arrow landing on 4?

1

Q12c(i)

....

(ii) What is the probability that it will not land on 5?

1

Q12c(ii)

....

Max. 6

Q 12
subtotal

13 a This year, the local football club raised £750 for charity.
It is to be shared between *Age Concern* and *Save the Children* in the ratio 2:3.
How much does each charity get?

b Last year, the football club only raised £600.
What was the percentage increase this year?

14 Here is the outline of a large house.

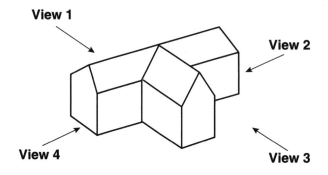

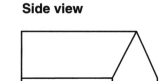

a Look at the side view of the house.
From which direction is it drawn?

b Sketch the view of the house from above.

15 These pie charts show information from a survey about computers at home. In the survey, 500 people in Brighton and 1000 people in Luton were asked about their use of computers at home.

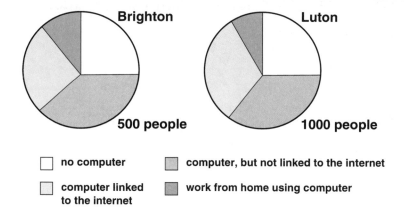

Brighton

Luton

500 people

1000 people

☐ no computer   ☐ computer, but not linked to the internet

☐ computer linked to the internet   ☐ work from home using computer

a Roughly what percentage of people in Brighton do not have a computer?

◆ 1 Q15a

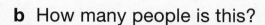

b How many people is this?

◆ 1 Q15b

Tom said, "The pie charts show that roughly the same number of people in Luton as in Brighton own computers but are not linked to the internet".

c Is this true? Explain your answer.

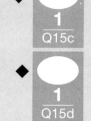

◆ 1 Q15c

◆ 1 Q15d

d What is the same in both charts about the number of people who don't own a computer?

Max. 11
Qs
13–15
subtotal

4
Q1

Test B
Levels 4–6

START
FINISH

CALCULATOR CAN BE USED

1 Here are some designs for badges.
Write the order of rotational symmetry under each one.

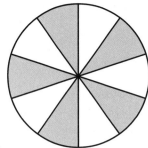

a .... **b** ....

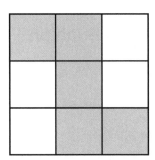

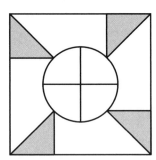

c .... **d** ....

2 Melissa has a mobile phone. During the day, calls cost 18p per minute.

a She makes calls for 15 minutes.
How much does this cost?

£ ....

1
Q2a

b During the evening, calls cost 6p per minute.
How many minutes does she get for £3.72?

1
Q2b

....

22

c Melissa has a £10 phone card to pay for the calls in
a and **b**.
Work out what value is left on the card after these calls.

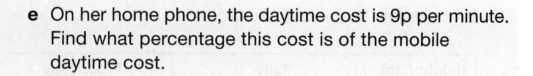

d The cost per minute for evening calls is what fraction
of the cost per minute for daytime calls?

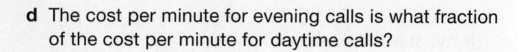

e On her home phone, the daytime cost is 9p per minute.
Find what percentage this cost is of the mobile
daytime cost.

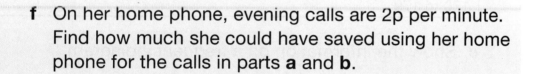

f On her home phone, evening calls are 2p per minute.
Find how much she could have saved using her home
phone for the calls in parts **a** and **b**.

3 Ranjit has collected data from the students in his class.

Height in centimetres

131	133	137	137	138	139	141	142	142	144
148	149	151	152	152	153	156	156	157	158
158	159	162	162	164	166	167	170	171	174

1
Q3a

a What is the median height?

....

2
Q3b

b Complete the frequency table.

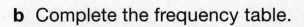

Height (cm)	Tally	Frequency
130 to 139		
140 to 149		
150 to 159		
160 to 169		
170 to 179		

2
Q3c

c Show the information on a frequency diagram.

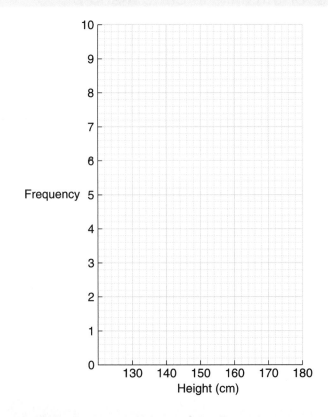

d State the modal group.

....

This diagram shows the heights of the students in another class.

e Make **two** comparisons with Ranjit's class.

....

....

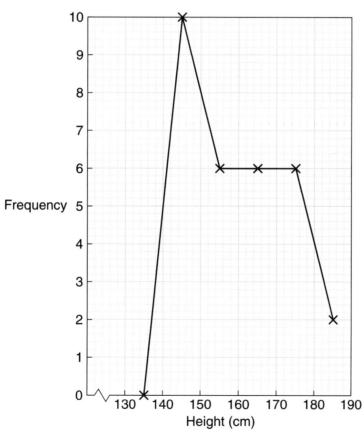

4   The numbers in the circles along each line add up to the number in the square on that line.

a Fill in the missing numbers in the square and the circle in the diagram below.

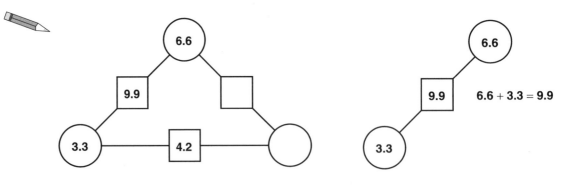

6.6 + 3.3 = 9.9

1
Q4a

2
Q4b

b Fill in the missing numbers in this diagram.

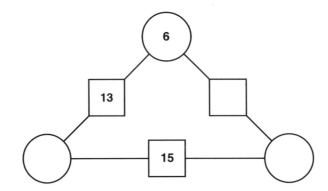

c Fill in the missing expressions in this diagram.

2
Q4c

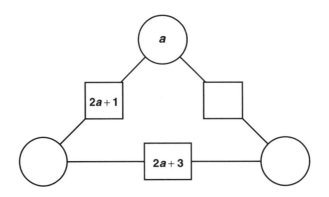

5 Maureen has measured her garden.
Her measurements are shown on the sketch.

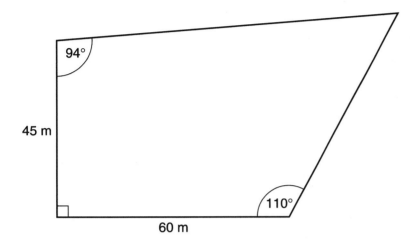

a Make an accurate scale drawing of the garden.
Use a scale of 1 cm to 10 m.

◆

4
Q5a

2
Q5b

b Measure the remaining angle and sides.

....

....

Max. 11
Qs 4–5
subtotal

6   **a** Plot the following graphs on the grid below.

      (i) Draw and label the graph of $y = 2x + 1$.

      (ii) Draw and label the graph of $y = 3 - x$.

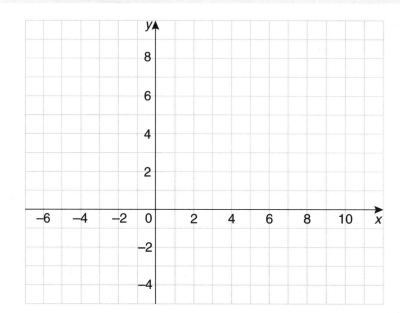

b Write down the co-ordinates of the point where the two graphs meet.

....

7   Daljit travels 21 000 miles each year on business.
She gets paid 36p per mile travelling expenses.

    a How much will she be paid?

....

    b Her car will use 0.14 litres of fuel for each mile she drives.
How many litres of fuel will she need to buy?

....

2
Q6a(i)

2
Q6a(ii)

1
Q6b

1
Q7a

1
Q7b

c Fuel costs 67.9p per litre.
What is the total cost of the fuel?

£ ....

d Show a rough calculation to check your answer to
part **c**.

....

8 Electrical fuses are sold in the following ratings:

3 amp   5 amp   13 amp

This formula gives the correct fuse to be fitted to an
appliance.

$F = \dfrac{P}{230}$ where F is the fuse in amps and P is the power
rating in watts.

Which fuse should you fit in a hairdryer with a power
rating of 1000 watts?

....

9 Look at questions **a–d** below and on the next page.
Write the name of the quadrilateral described.

a All sides equal, angles not all the same.

....

b Opposite sides equal, all angles equal.

....

Max. 14
Qs 6–9b
subtotal

c Only one pair of opposite sides parallel.

1 Q9c

....

d Only one diagonal is a line of symmetry.

1 Q9d

....

10 Below is a list of equations to solve.

a $3x - 2 = 7$

1 Q10a

....

b $4x + 5 = 2x - 7$

2 Q10b

....

c $7 - x = 2x + 4$

2 Q10c

....

11 Tom measures the rainfall each day for 10 days. His results in mm are: 2, 0, 0, 1, 7, 11, 5, 2, 0, 0

a What is the range?

1 Q11a

....

b What is the mode?

1 Q11b

....

c Calculate the median.

2
Q11c

....

d Calculate the mean.

1
Q11d

....

e Which average gives the best idea of the rainfall during these 10 days? Give a reason for your answer.

◆
1
Q11e

....

12 Prices in a clothes shop are increased by $\frac{2}{5}$.

   a What is the new price of a jacket that originally cost £50?

2
Q12a

....

In the sale, the prices are reduced to their original level.

b What percentage reduction is this?

◆
2
Q12b

....

Max. 17
Qs
9c–12
subtotal

Test C
Levels 5–7

START
FINISH

WITHOUT CALCULATOR

1 This rectangle has 2 axes of symmetry and rotational symmetry of order 2.

Describe the symmetry of these shapes.

2
Q1a

a A square

....

....

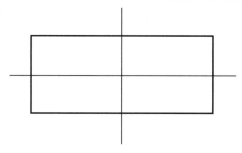

2
Q1b

b This hexagon

....

....

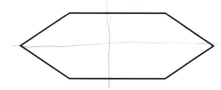

1
Q1c

c Sketch a shape that has two axes of symmetry and rotational symmetry of order 2 but is not a rectangle.

2 Look at this formula.

$$V = 10t - 13$$

a Find V when $t = 3$.

....

b Find the value of t when $V = 50$.

....

3 The number of apples picked from 25 young apple trees was recorded.

25	32	16	23	26
20	33	24	17	13
38	6	20	19	39
13	19	27	16	32
25	48	10	24	29

a Draw a stem-and-leaf diagram for these data.

stem	leaf
0	6
1	0 3 3 6 6 7 9 9
2	0 0 3 4 5 5 6 7 9
3	2 2 3 8 9
4	8

b Find the median number of apples.

.... 24 ....

Max. 11
Qs 1–3
subtotal

33

4   Solve the equations below.

a $2x = 5$

....

1
Q4a

b $2(x + 3) = 5$

....

2
Q4b

c $4 - 7x = 3(x - 10)$

....

2
Q4c

d Solve this inequality.

   $3x - 2 > 4x - 3$

....

....

2
Q4d

5   Joanna is saving for her holidays. She saves £15 each week.

a How many weeks will it be before she has more than £250?

....

2
Q5a

Wendy and William are also saving for their holidays. Their father gives them £20 each.

b Wendy saves £4 a week. After n weeks she has a total of £P. Write a formula connecting P and n.

....

1
Q5b

c William's total after n weeks is given by the formula

$$T = 20 + \frac{n^2}{10}$$

After how many weeks will Wendy and William have the same amount?

◆ **2** Q5c

....

....

6 **a** A rectangle is divided into three smaller rectangles and a square. The areas of three of the parts are shown on the diagram.
Find the area of the remaining rectangle.

◆ **2** Q6a

[diagram of rectangle with handwritten working]

95 cm²   25 cm²

228 cm²

[handwritten annotations: 19, 5, 12, 190, 228, 95, 25, 348, 60, 12, w² w² w², 3w² = 1200, 4² = 400, w = 20, L = 1200/300, w×L = 1200, 3w = L]

b Another rectangle has area 1200 cm².
Its width is one third of its length.
Use algebra to find its dimensions.

◆ **3** Q6b

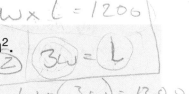

[handwritten: k = L ÷ 3, wL/3 = 1200, 3W = 1200/w, w × (3w) = 1200, w = 800]

....

[handwritten: 1w + 3L =]

....

Max. 17
Qs 4–6
subtotal

7 Find the lettered angles. In each case give a reason for your answer.

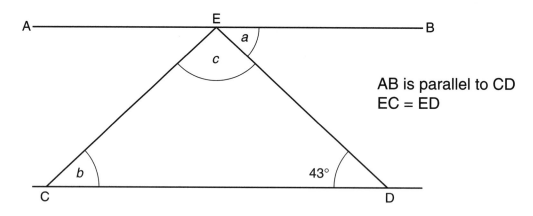

AB is parallel to CD
EC = ED

a Angle a = ...° Reason ....

b Angle b = ...° Reason ....

c Angle c = ...° Reason ....

8 Mr Smith has a briefcase with a combination lock.
There are three wheels on the lock.
Each wheel has ten positions, numbered 0 to 9.

   a The numbers to open the lock are 3, 1, 2 but Mr Smith has forgotten the order.

   (i) List all the possible combinations.

   ....

   (ii) What is the probability that he will get it right first time?

   ....

2
Q7a

2
Q7b

2
Q7c

2
Q8a(i)

1
Q8a(ii)

b To help him remember, he changes the numbers. The first is 1 and the other two add up to 7.

  (i) List all the possible combinations.

2
Q8b(i)

He remembers that no two digits are the same.

  (ii) What is the probability that he will get it right first time?

1
Q8b(ii)

  (iii) What is the probability that he will get it right in three attempts?

1
Q8b(iii)

9 Below are some fractions.

  a Arrange these fractions in size order, smallest first.

$$\frac{2}{3}, \frac{5}{8}, \frac{5}{6}, \frac{13}{24}$$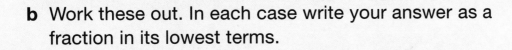

2
Q9a

  b Work these out. In each case write your answer as a fraction in its lowest terms.

  (i) $\frac{2}{3} + \frac{5}{8} =$ ....

2
Q9b(i)

  (ii) $\frac{2}{3} \times \frac{5}{8} =$ ....

2
Q9b(ii)

Max. 19
Qs 7–9
subtotal

3
Q10

10 This trough is a prism with a trapezium as its cross section. The dimensions are in centimetres.

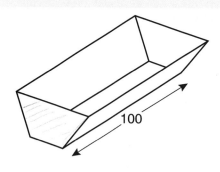

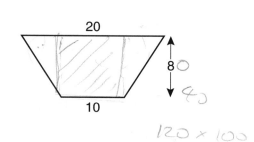

Calculate the volume.

....

....

1
Q11a

11 a John calculates the value of $\frac{0.137}{0.981}$ to be 0.134.

Without doing any calculation, explain how you know he is wrong.

....

1
Q11b(i)

b $\sqrt{26} = 5.1$ $\sqrt{2.6} = 1.6$ to one decimal place.

Use these to find the following.

1
Q11b(ii)

(i) $\sqrt{260}$ = ...

1
Q11b(iii)

(ii) $\sqrt{0.26}$ = ...

1
Q11b(iv)

(iii) $\sqrt{26\,000}$ = ...

38

(iv) $\sqrt{0.00026}$ = ...

12 Scientists have measured different breeds of penguin in the Antarctic.

Breed of penguin	Height (cm)	Mass (kg)
Emperor	114	29.5
King	94	15.9
Yellow-eyed	65	15.4
Fjordland	56	13.2
Southern Blue	40	11.0

a Draw a scatter graph for these data.

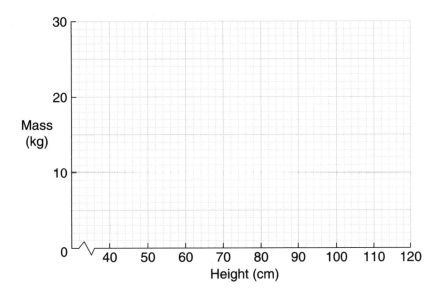

2
Q12a

b Describe the correlation.

....

1
Q12b

◆

c Another breed of penguin has a mass of 19 kg.
Estimate its height. Say how you found it.

2
Q12c

....

Max. 13
Qs
10–12
subtotal

....

4
Q1

Test D
Levels 5–7

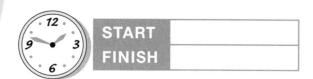

START

FINISH

CALCULATOR CAN BE USED

1 Here are some pictures of everyday objects.
Estimate the measurements.

.... cm   .... m

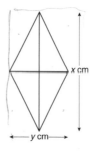

.... kg   .... g

2 The diagram shows a rhombus and the lengths of its diagonals.

x cm

←— *y* cm —→

1

Q2a(i)

a (i) Explain why the area is given by the formula
$A = \frac{1}{2}xy$.

....

(ii) Find A when $x = 17$ and $y = 7$.

....

◆
1
Q2a(ii)

(iii) Find x when $A = 7.56$ and $y = 2.7$.

....

1
Q2a(iii)

b (i) Write down the formula for the perimeter (P) of this rectangle.

x cm

$x + 2$ cm

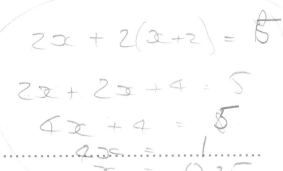

$2x + 2(x+2) = 5$

$2x + 2x + 4 = 5$

$4x + 4 = 5$

$2x =$

$x = 0.25$

2
Q2b(i)

....

....

(ii) Find P when $x = 24$.

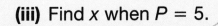

....

1
Q2b(ii)

(iii) Find x when $P = 5$.

....

1
Q2b(iii)

Max. 11
Qs 1–2
subtotal

Test D Levels 5–7

3 These pie charts show how land is used on two continents.

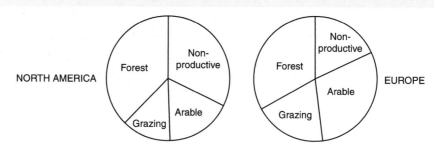

NORTH AMERICA — Forest, Non-productive, Arable, Grazing

EUROPE — Forest, Non-productive, Arable, Grazing

a Make two comparisons between the land use on these continents.

2
Q3a

....

....

b Mark thinks there is more arable land in Europe than in North America. Explain why this may not be true.

1
Q3b

....

4 This window is in the shape of a rectangle and a semicircle. The dimensions are in metres.

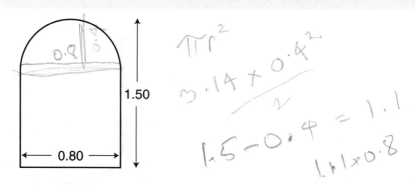

1.50

0.80

πr^2

3.14×0.4^2

$\frac{}{2}$

$1.5 - 0.4 = 1.1$

1.1×0.8

a Change 1.50 m into centimetres.

1
Q4a

....

b Change 0.80 m into millimetres.

....

c Make an accurate drawing of the window. Use a scale
of 1 cm to 20 cm.

◆

d Find the perimeter of the window.

....

e Find the area of the window.

....

Max. 13
Qs 3–4
subtotal

5 A supermarket sells AMAZ washing powder in three sizes.

7.5 kg	3 kg	690 g
£6.59	£2.59	65p

Which is the best value? Show how you decide.

7500g = 6.59

3000g = 2.59

690g = 0.65

6 A photograph is enlarged to make a poster.
The widths and heights are shown in centimetres.

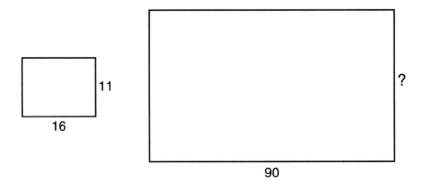

11

16

?

90

a How high is the poster?

b The photograph was enlarged from a negative.
The height of the negative is 24 mm.

How wide is the negative?

....

7 Look at these scatter diagrams.

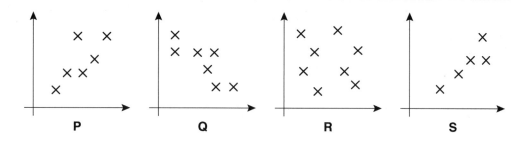

P   Q   R   S

a Describe the correlation in diagram S.

....

b Describe the correlation in diagram Q.

....

c Some students took both the Mathematics papers in
the Key Stage 3 Test.

Which diagram could show their results?

....

d Which diagram could show the value of a second-
hand car plotted against its age?

Max. 12
Qs 5–7
subtotal

45

....

8 The temperature C in °Celsius is connected to the temperature F in °Fahrenheit by the formula

$$C = \frac{5}{9}(F - 32)$$

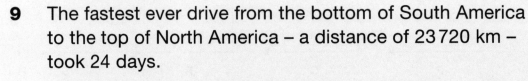

Find the temperature that has the same value in °C as °F.

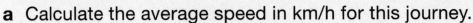

$9F = 5F - 160$

$4F = -160$

$F = -40$

9 The fastest ever drive from the bottom of South America to the top of North America – a distance of 23 720 km – took 24 days.

a Calculate the average speed in km/h for this journey.

b Estimate how long it would take to walk the same distance. Show all your workings and assumptions clearly.

46

10 The table shows the ages of 120 people living in a block of flats.

Age	Frequency
Up to 10	17
10 and up to 20	7
20 and up to 30	37
30 and up to 40	13
40 and up to 50	8
50 and up to 60	12
60 and up to 70	26

a Calculate an estimate of the mean age.

....

....

3
Q10a

b Estimate the median age. Show how you found it.

....

....

2
Q10b

c The people in another block of flats have a mean age of 35 and a median age of 35.

Compare the two age distributions.

....

....

2
Q10c

Max. **14**
Qs 8–10
subtotal

11 The distances marked on the sides of this triangle are in metres.
Find its area.

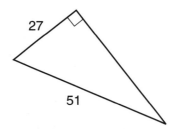

$\dfrac{3}{\text{Q11}}$

....

12 a Solve the following equations.

(i) $4x - 3(x - 2) = 0$

$\dfrac{2}{\text{Q12a(i)}}$

....

(ii) $\frac{1}{2}(3 - x) = x + 2$

$\dfrac{2}{\text{Q12a(ii)}}$

....

b Solve these simultaneous equations.

$3x + 4y = 7$

$x - 2y = -6$

$\dfrac{3}{\text{Q12b}}$

....

....

START

FINISH

WITHOUT CALCULATOR

1 Pat wants to make a scale model of a tent.
She uses a scale where 8 cm represents 5 feet.

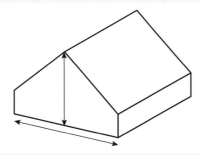

   a The width of the tent is 8 feet.
     What is the width of the model?

2
Q1a

....

   b The height of the model is 5 cm.
     What is the height of the real tent?

2
Q1b

....

2 The mean weight of 10 men is 75 kg.
The mean weight of 15 women is 50 kg.

What is the mean weight of all 25 people?

3
Q2

1
Q3a

....

3 Estimate the values of these expressions. Show
your working.

1
Q3b

   a $\dfrac{64.7 \times 18.3}{27.4}$ ....

Max. 9
Qs 1–3
subtotal

   b $\dfrac{0.73 \times 56.2}{18.7 - 7.9}$ ....

49

4 Jenny has two dogs, Rover and Tiny.
Rover eats $\frac{3}{5}$ of a tin of food each day.

a How many tins will Rover need for a week?

....

The dogs also have some biscuits.
Between them, they eat 600 g a day.
This is divided in the ratio Rover : Tiny = 3 : 1.

b How much biscuit does Rover eat in a day?

....

Tiny eats $\frac{1}{4}$ of a tin of food a day.

c Work out what fraction of a tin Rover and Tiny eat
between them each day.

....

5 Dillon and Karl are testing six-sided dice. They decide
Dillon's dice is fair.

a What is the probability that Dillon will throw a 6
next time?

....

Karl's dice is biased. He works out these probabilities.

Number on dice	1	2	3	4	5	6
Probability	0.2	0.1	0.1		0.2	0.1

b Work out the probability that Karl throws a 4.

....

c They both throw their dice.
   (i) Find the probability that they both throw a 6.

....

   (ii) Find the probability that one of them throws a 6.

◆

....

6 Look at this grid.

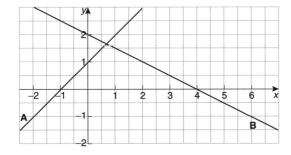

a Draw the line with equation $y = x - 1$. Label it **C**.

b Find the equation of line **B**.

....

c Use the graphs to solve the simultaneous equations:

$$x - y = -1$$
$$x + 2y = 4$$

....

7 *n* is an integer.

1
Q7a

a Explain why 2*n* − 1 is an odd number.

....

3
Q7b

b Multiply two consecutive odd numbers. Add 1 to the result. Prove that this is a multiple of 4.

....

....

8 Two goats live in this small field.

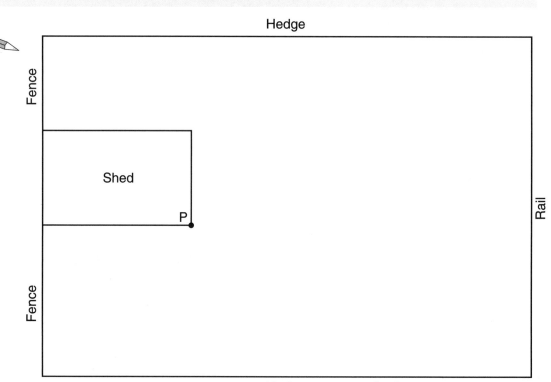

Hedge

Fence

Fence

Shed

P

Rail

Hedge   *Scale: 1 cm represents 1 m*

Nanny is fastened to the rail.

Her rope is 5 metres long. The end fastened to the rail can slide along the rail from one side of the field to the other.

a Mark accurately on the diagram where Nanny can go.

◆

Billy is also tied to a 5 m rope.

The other end of his rope is fastened to the corner of the shed at P.

b Mark accurately on the diagram where Billy can go.

◆

c Show clearly where they both can go.

◆

9 Multiply out the brackets and simplify the following:

a $3(x - 2) + 4(2x - 3)$

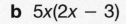

b $5x(2x - 3)$

c $x(2x + 5) - 3x(x - 2)$

Max. 13
Qs 7–9
subtotal

10 Complete the questions below, showing your answers on this diagram.

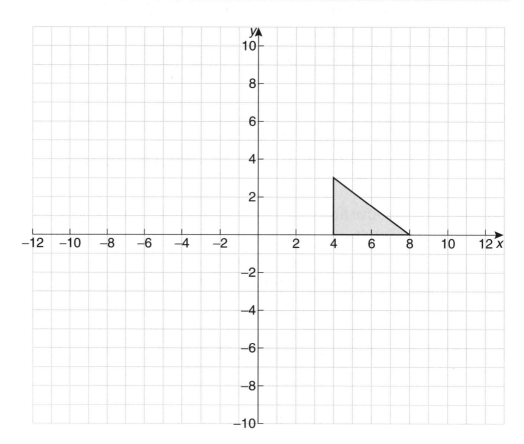

2
Q10a

2
Q10b

2
Q10c

a Rotate the shaded triangle about the origin through 90° anticlockwise. Label it A.

b Reflect the shaded triangle in $x = -1$. Label it B.

c Enlarge the shaded triangle with centre the origin and scale factor $\frac{1}{2}$. Label it C.

11 The cumulative frequency graphs show how long electric lamps lasted. There are samples from two different makes, **A** and **B**.

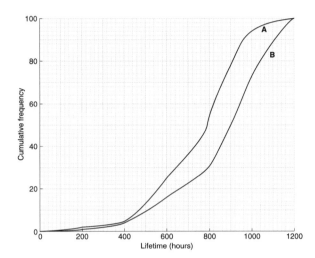

a How many lamps are there in each sample?

....

◆ 1
Q11a

b For sample **A**, find:

(i) the median

....

1
Q11b(i)

(ii) the interquartile range

....

2
Q11b(ii)

(iii) how many lamps were still working after 900 hours

....

1
Q11b(iii)

◆ 1
Q11c

c Which lamp would you buy? Give a reason.

A ☐ B ☐

....

Max. 12
Qs 10–11
subtotal

12 Look at this right-angled triangle.

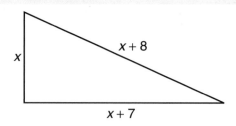

a Use Pythagoras' theorem to form an equation in x.

....

b Simplify your equation.

....

c Solve the equation.

....

13 In triangle ABC, F is the midpoint of AB. FE is parallel to BC. DE is parallel to BA.
Prove that triangles AFE and EDC are congruent.

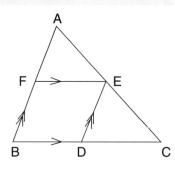

....

1
Q12a

2
Q12b

2
Q12c

4
Q13

◆

Max. 9
Qs
12–13
subtotal

56

Ask a friend or a parent to detach page 59 and read the questions for Test 1 to you. Each question will be read twice and you will then have a short time to complete your answer. For questions 1 to 6 it will be 5 seconds, for questions 7 to 20 you will have 10 seconds and for questions 21 to 30, 15 seconds. Any data you require is contained in the blue-tinted box. **You only need a pen or pencil. You must not use a calculator, ruler or any other geometrical instruments.**

Write your answers on the lines below.

1	18 37	**18**	5 10 11	
2		**19**	$2\frac{1}{2}$ 80	
3 .... ml		**20** 30 g 300 g		
4		3000 g 30 kg		
		300 kg 3000 kg		
5	11:15 12:30	**21**	25 21 28 17 32	
6	$2x = 36$	**22** ....km/h	210 $1\frac{3}{4}$	
7	$5x - 5y$	**23**	$\frac{2}{5} + \frac{1}{3}$	
8	$247 \div 0.43$	**24**	30	

9 30 mm   30 cm
  30 m   30 km
  30 g   30 kg

Pie chart labelled: Walk, Car, Bus

10	$\frac{1}{2}x = 4$	**25** £		
11 .... m	12.5 5			
12	0.2			

Cuboid dimensions: 4, 5, 2

13	2% 1000	**26**	0.2 0.1	
14		**27**	30 120	
15	4349	**28**		

Right triangle: 5, 13

16	$x^2 - x = 0$	**29**	$703 \div 19 = 37$	
17 ....°	65° 37°	**30**	0.85	

Ask a friend or a parent to detach page 60 and read the questions for Test 2 to you. Each question will be read twice and you will then have a short time to complete your answer. For questions 1 to 6 it will be 5 seconds, for questions 7 to 20 you will have 10 seconds and for questions 21 to 30, 15 seconds. Any data you require is contained in the blue-tinted box. **You only need a pen or pencil. You must not use a calculator, ruler or any other geometrical instruments.**

Write your answers on the lines below.

1	
2	3.7 1.9
3 ....cm	$7\frac{1}{2}$
4	
5	
6	0.065
7	3.017
8	
9 ....hours	100 50
10	$5x - 3$
11	14, 9, 4, …
12	10 g 1 kg
13	2:3
14	0.05
15	150% 30
16	1 min 35 s 5 min 3 s, 52 s

17	$\frac{35}{210}$
18	$x < -10$
19 ....cm	
20 ....%	£5 £4
21 ....cm^2	3 cm 5 cm 4 cm
22	7 15 0 12 6
23	$83 \times 41 = 3403$ 10 209
24 ....m	75 m^2
25 ....°	110° 73° 90°
26	$\frac{3}{10} \times \frac{2}{15}$
27	3^2 2^3
28	$29^3 = 24\ 389$
29 ....s	3 8
30	

58

Mental Mathematics Test 1:
Questions

INSTRUCTIONS

Detach this page from the book.

Read each question, exactly as printed, twice.

Allow a short time for each answer to be written down (on page 57).

For questions 1 to 6 allow 5 seconds, for questions 7 to 20 allow 10 seconds and for questions 21 to 30 allow 15 seconds.

1 Subtract eighteen from thirty-seven.

2 What number, divided by seven, gives eight?

3 How many millilitres are there in two and a half litres?

4 What is one hundred squared?

5 How many minutes is it from eleven fifteen to twelve thirty?

6 Two x equals thirty-six. What is x?

7 x minus y is three. What is five x minus five y?

8 What is the approximate value of the expression on your answer sheet?

9 Circle the measurement that is about the same as one foot.

10 Solve the equation on the answer sheet.

11 A tree trunk is twelve point five metres long. It is cut into five equal pieces. How long is each?

12 Work out nought point two squared.

13 What is two percent of one thousand?

14 What is the probability that a fair coin will land heads three times in a row?

15 Write the number four thousand, three hundred and forty-nine correct to two significant figures.

16 Solve the equation on your answer sheet.

17 Two angles of a triangle are sixty-five degrees and thirty-seven degrees. What is the third angle?

18 The mean of five numbers is ten. Another number is included. The new mean is eleven. What is the other number?

19 A bottle of milk will fill two and a half glasses. How many bottles are needed to fill eighty glasses?

20 Circle the mass that could be that of a holiday suitcase.

21 Find the median of the numbers on your answer sheet.

22 A car travelled two hundred and ten kilometres in one and three-quarter hours. What was its average speed?

23 Add the fractions on your answer sheet.

24 The pie chart shows how thirty students came to school. About how many walked?

25 A block of precious metal measures five by four by two centimetres. It costs one hundred pounds a cubic centimetre. How much is the block worth?

26 Work out nought point two divided by nought point one.

27 What is thirty as a percentage of one hundred and twenty?

28 What is the length of the third side of the triangle on your answer sheet?

29 Seven hundred and three divided by nineteen is thirty-seven. What is three point seven times nineteen?

30 Write down a fraction equal to nought point eight five.

Mental Mathematics Test 2:
Questions

INSTRUCTIONS

Detach this page from the book.

Read each question, exactly as printed, twice.

Allow a short time for each answer to be written down (on page 58).

For questions 1 to 6 allow 5 seconds, for questions 7 to 20 allow 10 seconds and for questions 21 to 30 allow 15 seconds.

1   Divide ten by five and then add two.

2   Work out three point seven minus one point nine.

3   How many centimetres are there in seven and a half metres?

4   Divide seventy-two by eight.

5   Multiply two by three by five by seven.

6   What number is one hundred times bigger than nought point nought six five?

7   Write the number three point nought one seven correct to two decimal places.

8   How many edges has a cube?

9   A car travelling at one hundred kilometres an hour completes a journey in x hours. How long will it take to complete the journey at fifty kilometres an hour.

10 What is the value of five x minus three when x equals two?

11 Write down the next number in the sequence fourteen, nine, four, …

12 What is ten grams as a fraction of a kilogram?

13 The ratio of apples to oranges in a fruit bowl is two to three. There are six apples. How many oranges are there?

14 The probability that my train will be late is nought point nought five. What is the probability that it will be on time?

15 Find one hundred and fifty percent of thirty.

16 I made three telephone calls lasting one minute thirty-five seconds, five minutes and three seconds and fifty-two seconds. What was the total time?

17 Write the fraction on the answer sheet in its lowest terms.

18 Write down a value of x which satisfies the inequality on your answer sheet.

19 Estimate the length of the line on your answer sheet.

20 The price of a ticket falls from £5 to £4. What percentage reduction is this?

21 Work out the area of the triangle on your answer sheet.

22 The answer sheet shows the number of points scored by a rugby player in five matches. Find the mean number of points.

23 Use the calculation on your answer sheet to work out how many forty-ones there are in ten thousand two hundred and nine.

24 A circular pond has area seventy-five square metres. Roughly what is its diameter?

25 Three angles of a quadrilateral are one hundred and ten, seventy-three and ninety. What is the fourth angle?

26 Multiply the fractions on your answer sheet.

27 Add together three to the power two and two to the power three.

28 Use the calculation on your answer sheet to work out the value of nought point two nine cubed.

29 Divide three minutes into eight equal parts. How many seconds in each?

30 A pilot steers a ship so that the distances from two marker buoys remain equal. Describe the ship's course.

Answers

HOW TO MARK THE TESTS

When marking the tests remember that the answers given are sample answers. You must look at your answers and judge whether they deserve credit. If they do, then award the mark. Although you should always try to spell words accurately, do not mark any answer wrong because the words are misspelt.

In these answers, the calculation is often given as well as the answer. Sometimes the method earns credit (e.g. Question 10b in Test B), but other times only the answer itself earns credit (e.g. Question 5a in Test A). In the latter cases, the working out has been provided to help you understand how to arrive at the correct answer.

When you go through the answers, try to work out where you have gone wrong. Make a note of the key points, so that you will remember them next time.

Only count the marks you scored in one hour on each test. Enter your marks for each test on the Marking grid on page 79, and then work out your level of achievement in these tests on page 78.

Test A Pages 12–21

1	**a**	multiple	*1 mark*
	b	square	*1 mark*
	c	factor	*1 mark*

TOTAL 3 MARKS

 **Examiner's tip**   Make sure you do not confuse multiple and factor.

2 a 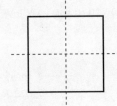   **b** 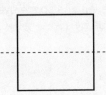   **c**   **d**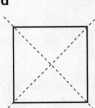

1 mark each: 4 marks

TOTAL 4 MARKS

 **Examiner's tip**   There must be no extra lines drawn!

3

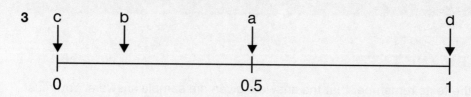

c   b   a   d

0   0.5   1

1 mark each: 4 marks

TOTAL 4 MARKS

4   Shape (c) is similar to the shaded shape.   *1 mark*
       Shape (d) is congruent to the shaded shape.   *1 mark*

TOTAL 2 MARKS

Remember, 'similar' means same shape, different size; 'congruent' means exactly the same shape and size.

5 a   43   *1 mark*
   b $F = 2A + 9$ *1 mark*
   c   14   *1 mark*

TOTAL 3 MARKS

Don't forget the '$F = $' is an important part of the formula and should not be left out.

6 a   430   *1 mark*
   b   62   *1 mark*
   c   70   *1 mark*
   d   100   *1 mark*
   e   1000   *1 mark*
   f   9.4   *1 mark*
   g   100   *1 mark*
   h   380   *1 mark*

TOTAL 8 MARKS

Remember that a number moves to the left one space every time you multiply by 10, and one to the right when you divide by 10.

7 a (i)   650 mm, 1070 mm   *1 mark*
    (ii)   0.65 m, 1.07 m   *1 mark*
   b   2 feet   *1 mark*
          $3\frac{1}{2}$ feet   *1 mark*

TOTAL 4 MARKS

You are expected to know that 1 foot is about 30 cm.

| 8 | Brand B | 1 mark |
| | Although it has a lower mean, it has a much narrower range | 1 mark |

TOTAL 2 MARKS

Examiner's tip

Although Brand A lasts longer on average, some of them will not last as long as those in Brand B. Brand B is more reliable/consistent. If you bought a lot of batteries, Brand A would be better.

| 9 | a | £7.65 | 2 marks |
| | b | £6.12 | 2 marks |

TOTAL 4 MARKS

Examiner's tip

In each part there will be one mark for a correct method, e.g.

$$\begin{array}{r} 45 \\ \times 17 \\ \hline 450 \\ 315 \end{array}$$

and multiplying by 0.8 for part **b**.

10	a	$c + 7d$	1 mark
	b	$2x - 4y$	1 mark
	c	$15 - (-2)(-4) = 15 - 8$	1 mark
		$\qquad\qquad\qquad = 7$	1 mark
	d (i)	$x = 30$	1 mark
	(ii)	$3x = -3$	1 mark
		$x = -1$	1 mark

TOTAL 7 MARKS

Examiner's tip

In part **d(i)** you should not be tempted to divide both sides by 3.

| 11 | $558 + 42 = 600$ | 2 marks |

TOTAL 2 MARKS

Examiner's tip

Award 2 marks if all correct. Award 1 mark if the digits in the units column add up to 10.

12 a (i) $\frac{1}{5}$ or 0.2 or 20%   *1 mark*

   (ii) $\frac{3}{5}$ or 0.6 or 60%   *1 mark*

   b (i) Too few results to be reliable   *1 mark*
   (ii) $\frac{23}{100}$ or 0.23 or 23%   *1 mark*

   c (i) 0.25   *1 mark*
   (ii) 0.75   *1 mark*

TOTAL 6 MARKS

These answers show the only acceptable ways of writing probabilities. The answers to part **c** are found by subtracting from 1.

13 a £300, £450   *1 + 1 marks*
   b 25%   *1 mark*

TOTAL 3 MARKS

In part **a**, if you did not get the answers right, you will score 1 mark for using either two or three fifths. In part **b**, dividing 150 by 600 will earn 1 mark.

14 a View 2   *1 mark*
   b   *3 marks*

TOTAL 4 MARKS

In part **b**, there could be one mark for the correct shape of the outline, one mark for the rooftops and one mark for the joins of the roofs.

15 a 25%   *1 mark*
   b 125 (people)   *1 mark*
   c Not correct because although percentages are similar, the number of
       people interviewed is not the same   *1 mark*
   d The same percentage of people surveyed in both towns   *1 mark*

TOTAL 4 MARKS

The wording in part **c** can be different but the argument/reason must mention the different sample sizes.

TEST TOTAL 60 MARKS

1 **a** 5   **b** 6
   c 2   **d** 4

1 mark for each answer: 4 marks

TOTAL 4 MARKS

Examiner's tip To find the order of rotational symmetry, count how many times the object fits on itself as you turn it. Don't forget to include the original position.

2 **a** £2.70   *1 mark*
   b 62   *1 mark*
   c £3.58   *1 mark*
   d $\frac{1}{3}$ *1 mark*
   e 50%   *1 mark*
   f $9 \times 15 + 4 \times 62 = 383$
      £3.83   *1 mark*

TOTAL 6 MARKS

Examiner's tip It is easier to use the differences between the rates to find how much is saved in part **f**.

3 **a** 152.5   *1 mark*
   b Frequency: 6, 6, 10, 5, 3   *2 marks*
   c Bar graph (bars across 130–140, 140–150, etc.) or a polygon
      (points at 135, 145, etc.)   *1 mark*
      Heights plotted the same as your answer to part **b**   *1 mark*
   d 150 to 159   *1 mark*
   e Ranjit's class has a higher modal group.   *1 mark*
      The shortest pupils are in Ranjit's class *or* the tallest are in the other class.   *1 mark*

TOTAL 8 MARKS

Examiner's tip As there are an even number of heights, the median is between the middle two, 152 and 153. Your comparisons in part **e** should be about the heights, not the shape of the graph.

4 **a**   **b**   **c**

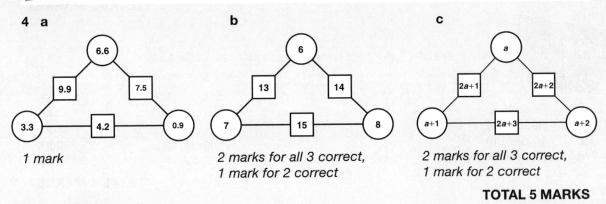

1 mark   *2 marks for all 3 correct,*   *2 marks for all 3 correct,*
         1 mark for 2 correct   *1 mark for 2 correct*

TOTAL 5 MARKS

Examiner's tip Check by adding your answers in the circles at the end of each line.

5 a   Three angles and two sides accurately drawn   *4 marks*

    b   Angle = 66°   *1 mark*

            Other sides = 7.9 and 5.4 cm (or 79 and 54 m, full size)   *1 mark*

TOTAL 6 MARKS

Ask someone to check the accuracy of your drawing. The angles should be within 1° and the lengths within 1 mm of the stated sizes. If you have drawn it accurately, you should get these other measurements, to the same accuracy.

6 a (i)   Straight line passing through (0, 1) and (4, 9)   *1 + 1 marks*

    (ii)   Straight line passing through (0, 3) and (3, 0)   *1 + 1 marks*

    b   (0.7, 2.3)   *1 mark*

TOTAL 5 MARKS

Your lines should be ruled carefully and reach at least as far as the points indicated. If drawn accurately the lines will meet at the given point, reading to the nearest 0.1.

7 a   £7560   *1 mark*

    b   2940 litres   *1 mark*

    c   £1996.26   *1 mark*

    d   20 000 × 0.1 × 1 = 2000   *2 marks*

TOTAL 5 MARKS

There are other possible answers to part **d**. Make the numbers as simple as possible but without moving too far from the original size. One way to do this is shown. Since 0.14 is multiplied by 0.679, making one smaller and the other larger keeps the result about right. You will score one mark for an attempt to round the numbers, e.g. 21 000 × 0.15 × 0.68 – but not easy to work out in the head!

8   1000 ÷ 230 = 4.35   *1 mark*

      5 amp   *1 mark*

TOTAL 2 MARKS

Show the result of your calculation as well as the size of the fuse.

9 a   Rhombus   *1 mark*

    b   Rectangle   *1 mark*

    c   Trapezium   *1 mark*

    d   Kite (or arrowhead)   *1 mark*

TOTAL 4 MARKS

Apart from part **d**, there is only one answer in each case. An arrowhead is not a convex polygon but it has the same properties as a kite.

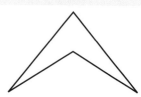

10 a $x = 3$ *1 mark*

   b $2x = -12$ *1 mark*

        $x = -6$ *1 mark*

   c $3 = 3x$ or $-3x = -3$ *1 mark*

        $x = 1$ *1 mark*

                                               TOTAL 5 MARKS

Examiner's tip   The correct solutions will earn both marks in parts **b** and **c**. However, it is a good idea to write down all the steps in the solution to equations, in case you make a mistake.

11 a   11 (millimetres)   *1 mark*

   b   0 (millimetres)   *1 mark*

   c   1.5 (millimetres)   *2 marks*

   d   2.8 (millimetres)   *1 mark*

   e   Median – e.g. because it ignores the high value

        or Mean – e.g. because it gives a good indication of the amount of rain   *1 mark*

                                               TOTAL 6 MARKS

Examiner's tip   In **e** the mode is not a good average to use as only 4 days had no rain. Either median or mean with a valid reason would gain the mark.

12 a   £70   *2 marks*

   b   28.6%   *2 marks*

                                               TOTAL 4 MARKS

Examiner's tip   In each part there is a mark for the method if you got the answer wrong, e.g. $50 + \frac{2}{5} \times 50$ and $\frac{20}{70} \times 100$. Remember to use the price before the sale in part **b**.

                                             TEST TOTAL 60 MARKS

Test C   Pages 32–39

1 a   Four axes   *1 mark*

        Order 4   *1 mark*

   b   Two axes   *1 mark*

        Order 2   *1 mark*

   c   Rhombus

                                               1 mark

                                               TOTAL 5 MARKS

Examiner's tip   The shape in part **c** does not have to be a quadrilateral, as the answer to part **b** shows!

2 a 17 · *1 mark*
  b 6.3 · *1 mark*

TOTAL 2 MARKS

In part **b**, 13 must be added to the 50 before dividing by 10.

3 a   2 | 5   means 25 · *1 mark*

```
0 | 6                              0 | 6
1 | 6 7 3 9 3 9 6 0                1 | 0 3 3 6 6 7 9 9
2 | 5 3 6 0 4 0 7 5 4 9           2 | 0 0 3 4 4 5 5 6 7 9
3 | 2 3 8 9 2                      3 | 2 2 3 8 9
4 | 8                              4 | 8
```
· *2 marks*

  b   Median = 24 · *1 mark*

TOTAL 4 MARKS

The stem-and-leaf diagram for part **a** should be ordered (as above right). The diagram above left is a working diagram, but you can still score both marks even if you don't use a working diagram.

The median in part **b** is the 13th number in the ordered stem-and-leaf diagram.

4 a $x = 2\frac{1}{2}$ · *1 mark*

  b $2x + 6 = 5$ or $x + 3 = 2\frac{1}{2}$ · · · · · · · · · · · · · · · · · *1 mark*

       $x = -\frac{1}{2}$ · *1 mark*

  c $4 - 7x = 3x - 30$ · *1 mark*

       $x = 3.4$ · *1 mark*

  d $-x > -1$ or $1 > x$ · *1 mark*

       $x < 1$ · *1 mark*

TOTAL 7 MARKS

Great care is needed with the negative signs in part **d**. $1 > x$ is a satisfactory solution but it is usual to finish with x on the left.

5 a   17 · *2 marks*
  b $P = 4n + 20$ · *1 mark*
  c $4n + 20 = 20 + \frac{n^2}{10}$ · *1 mark*

       $n = 40$ · *1 mark*

TOTAL 5 MARKS

Remember to show the method in part **a**. The answer is not 16 as she will not have reached £250 by then, only £240. There is another solution in part **c**, $n = 0$ (they both start with £20).

6 a   Finding width and height of rectangle (5 cm and 19 cm)   *1 mark*

      60 cm²   *1 mark*

b $3x^2 = 1200$ *1 mark*

      $x^2 = 400$ *1 mark*

      20 and 60   *1 mark*

TOTAL 5 MARKS

Examiner's tip   The starting point in part **a** must be the square. Other ways involve guessing.

7 a   43°   *1 mark*

      alternate angles between AB and CD   *1 mark*

b   43°   *1 mark*

      isosceles triangle ECD   *1 mark*

c   94°   *1 mark*

      angles of a triangle add up to 180°   *1 mark*

TOTAL 6 MARKS

Examiner's tip   Don't be tempted to measure the angles on the test paper, as they are far from accurate! Use the information given. Alternate angles between parallel lines are sometimes called Z angles.

8 a (i)   123, 132, 213, 231, 312, 321   *2 marks*

     (ii) $\frac{1}{6}$ *1 mark*

   b (i)   107, 170, 116, 161, 125, 152, 134, 143   *2 marks*

     (ii) $\frac{1}{6}$ *1 mark*

     (iii) $\frac{3}{6}$ or $\frac{1}{2}$ *1 mark*

TOTAL 7 MARKS

Examiner's tip   You may make one error and still score one mark in each of parts **a(i)** and **b(i)**. Be systematic in writing them down as this will help you not to miss one or repeat one, both of which will lose a mark. In part **b(ii)**, two combinations have one repeated so are not included when calculating the probability.

9 a $\frac{13}{24}$, $\frac{5}{8}$ $\left(=\frac{15}{24}\right)$, $\frac{2}{3}$ $\left(=\frac{16}{24}\right)$, $\frac{5}{6}$ $\left(=\frac{20}{24}\right)$ *1 mark for correct equivalent fractions,*
1 mark for correct order   *2 marks*

   b (i) $\frac{16}{24} + \frac{15}{24} =$ *1 mark*

       $\frac{31}{24}$ or $1\frac{7}{24}$ *1 mark*

     (ii) $\frac{2 \times 5}{3 \times 8} = \frac{10}{24}$ *1 mark*

        $= \frac{5}{12}$ *1 mark*

TOTAL 6 MARKS

Examiner's tip   The methods for combining fractions are shown above and earn marks.

10 Area of trapezium = 120 cm²   *1 mark*
       Volume = 120 × 100 = 12 000 cm³   *1 + 1 marks*

TOTAL 3 MARKS

Use the formulae given on page 8 for the area of the trapezium and the volume of the prism.

11 a Dividing by a number less than 1 increases the size of a number   *1 mark*
  b (i) 16   *1 mark*
    (ii) 0.51   *1 mark*
    (iii) 160   *1 mark*
    (iv) 0.016   *1 mark*

TOTAL 5 MARKS

Notice that the square root of a number less than 1 is larger than the original number.

12 a Scatter graph plotted   *2 marks*

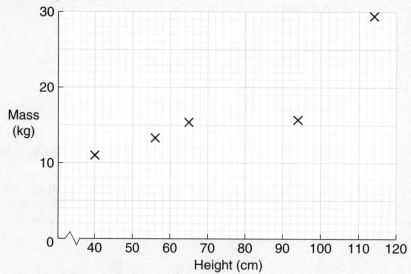

  b Positive   *1 mark*
  c Between 80 and 100   *1 mark*
       Read from a line of best fit or from the nearest point   *1 mark*

TOTAL 5 MARKS

It is not a strong positive correlation. A line of best fit will tend to ignore the point for the King penguin. If you use this for part **c**, your answer should be near 80.

TEST TOTAL 60 MARKS

1   15 to 30 cm   4 to 6 m   *1 + 1 marks*
        1 to 2 kg   8 to 15 g   *1 + 1 marks*

TOTAL 4 MARKS

Examiner's tip   You can check these afterwards but be careful with the bus!

2 **a (i)** The rhombus is half a rectangle measuring x by y.   *1 mark*
     (ii) 59.5 cm²   *1 mark*
    (iii) 5.6   *1 mark*
  b (i) $x + x + 2 + x + x + 2$ *1 mark*
           $4x + 4$ or $4(x + 1)$ *1 mark*
   (ii) 100   *1 mark*
   (iii) 0.25 or $\frac{1}{4}$ *1 mark*

TOTAL 7 MARKS

Examiner's tip   The simplified expression will earn both marks in part **b(i)**.

3 **a** Proportion of Forest and Grazing about the same   *1 mark*
      More Arable in Europe or more Non-productive in North America   *1 mark*
   b The total area of North America is not the same as the total area of Europe. *1 mark*

TOTAL 3 MARKS

Examiner's tip   You may have some different answers in part **a**. When asked to make two comparisons, look for what is the same and what is different.

4 **a** 150 cm   *1 mark*
   b 800 mm   *1 mark*
   c   Accurate drawing: lengths 4 cm and 7.5 cm   *1 mark*
              right angles   *1 mark*
              semicircle radius 2 cm   *1 mark*
   d $\frac{1}{2} \times \pi \times 0.8$ for semicircle   *1 mark*

       5.06 m   *1 mark*
   e $\frac{1}{2} \times \pi \times 0.4^2$ *1 mark*

       0.8 × 1.5   *1 mark*
       1.45 m²   *1 mark*

TOTAL 10 MARKS

Examiner's tip   The answers to parts **d** and **e** are given correct to three significant figures. You would not lose marks here for giving more figures but it would not be sensible from the measurements given in the question.

5 $6.59 \div 7.5 = 0.879$ *1 mark*
          $2.59 \div 3 = 0.863$ *1 mark*
          $0.65 \div 0.69 = 0.942$ *1 mark*
          The 3 kg box is best as it costs less per kilogram.   *1 mark*

TOTAL 4 MARKS

You could instead calculate how much washing powder you get for £1 or 1p. The largest number will then represent the best buy.

6 a $90 \div 16 \times 11$ *1 mark*
          61.875, or 61.9 or 62 cm   *1 mark*
   b $24 \times 16 \div 11$ *1 mark*
          34.9 or 35 mm   *1 mark*

TOTAL 4 MARKS

The data in the question is to the nearest centimetre/millimetre, so similar accuracy is sensible for the answers. Notice that it is not necessary to convert the millimetres into centimetres in part **b**, as this is a proportional calculation and gives an answer also in millimetres.

7 a   (Strong) positive correlation   *1 mark*
   b   Negative correlation   *1 mark*
   c   P (or possibly S)   *1 mark*
   d   Q   *1 mark*

TOTAL 4 MARKS

8   Put $F = C$ $9C = 5(C - 32)$ *1 mark*
                          $4C = -160$ $C = -40$ *1 mark*

TOTAL 2 MARKS

You could just as well put $C = F$ and solve for F. The result should be the same!

9 a $\dfrac{23\,720}{24 \times 24} = 41.18$ km/h   *2 marks*
   b   e.g. 'Average' walking speed is 6 km/h   *1 mark*
          Drive speed is approximately 42 km/h
          Ratio of speeds = 42:6 = 7:1
          Ratio of times = 1:7
          Therefore walking takes $7 \times 24 = 168$ days   *2 marks*

TOTAL 5 MARKS

In **b** the time would be a guide to the minimum. There is a range of possible assumptions. Examiners would give credit for sensible assumptions and a time between 160 and 240 days.

10 a   Using midpoints 5, 15, 25, 35, 45, 55, 65   *1 mark*
Multiplying these by the frequencies, adding and dividing by 120   *1 mark*
35.7 years   *1 mark*

b   29 or 30 years   *1 mark*
Median between 60th and 61st, at top of group 20 to 30   *1 mark*

c   Second more evenly distributed, or fewer old people   *1 mark*
Mean is almost the same   *1 mark*

TOTAL 7 MARKS

Examiner's tip   When the mean and the median are about the same size, the distribution is balanced and not weighted to an extreme. In the first case here, the 26 people over 60 caused the mean to be higher than the median.

11 $\sqrt{51^2 - 27^2}$ *1 mark*
$\sqrt{1872} \times 27 \div 2$ *1 mark*
584   *1 mark*

TOTAL 3 MARKS

Examiner's tip   In this question you have to recognise that the third side is needed to find the area and that Pythagoras' theorem is the way to find it. The correct answer would earn all 3 marks.

12 a (i) $4x - 3x + 6 = 0$ *1 mark*
$x = -6$ *1 mark*

(ii) $3 - x = 2x + 4$ *1 mark*
$3x = -1$
$x = -\frac{1}{3}$ *1 mark*

b $3x + 4y = 7$
$2x - 4y = -12$ (multiplying second equation by 2)   *1 mark*
$5x = -5$
$x = -1$ *1 mark*
$-1 - 2y = -6$ (substituting for x)
$y = 2\frac{1}{2}$ *1 mark*

TOTAL 7 MARKS

Examiner's tip   You could do part **b** by multiplying the second equation by 3 and then subtracting. This would give $10y = 25$.

TEST TOTAL 60 MARKS

Test E: Pages 49–56

1 a $8 \times \frac{8}{5}$ cm   *1 mark*
$= 12.8$ cm   *1 mark*

b $5 \times \frac{5}{8}$ feet   *1 mark*
$= 3\frac{1}{8}$ or 3.125 feet   *1 mark*

TOTAL 4 MARKS

2   Total weight of men = 750 kg

Total weight of women = 750 kg   *1 mark*

$1500 \div 25$ *1 mark*

= 60 kg   *1 mark*

TOTAL 3 MARKS

3 **a** $\dfrac{60 \times 20}{30} = 40$ *1 mark*

    b $\dfrac{0.7 \times 60}{10}$ or $\dfrac{0.8 \times 50}{10}$ *1 mark*

       = 4

TOTAL 2 MARKS

4 **a** $7 \times \frac{3}{5} = 4\frac{1}{5}$ *1 mark*

       5 tins needed   *1 mark*

    b $\frac{3}{4} \times 600$ *1 mark*

       = 450 g   *1 mark*

    c $\frac{3}{5} + \frac{1}{4} = \frac{12+5}{20}$ *1 mark*

       $= \frac{17}{20}$ *1 mark*

TOTAL 6 MARKS

5 **a** $\frac{1}{6}$ *1 mark*

    b 0.3   *1 mark*

    c (i) $\frac{1}{6} \times 0.1 = \frac{1}{60}$ *1 mark*

      (ii) $\frac{1}{6} \times 0.9 + \frac{5}{6} \times 0.1$ *1+1 mark*

         $\frac{9}{60} + \frac{5}{60} = \frac{14}{60} = \frac{7}{30}$ *1 mark*

TOTAL 6 MARKS

6 a 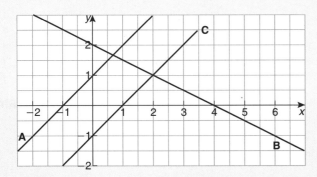   *1 mark*

b $x + 2y$ *1 mark*
     $= 4$ *1 mark*
c   Taking reading where A and B meet   *1 mark*
     $x = 0.7, y = 1.7$ *1 mark*

TOTAL 5 MARKS

 If you wanted to (and you had time!), you could check your answer by algebra.
This solution is $x = \frac{2}{3}$, $y = 1\frac{2}{3}$.

7 a $2n$ is even, as it is $2 \times$ an integer.
       1 less is the number before, which is odd.   *1 mark*
b   Consecutive odd numbers could be $2n - 1$ and $2n + 1$ *1 mark*
       $(2n - 1)(2n + 1) = 4n^2 - 1$ *1 mark*
       Add 1 to give $4n^2$, which is $4 \times$ an integer and therefore a multiple of 4.   *1 mark*

TOTAL 4 MARKS

 Notice how the first part of the question gave you a start. To prove that something
is true for all numbers, you must use a general case – here it is algebraic. It is no
good trying some specific examples, even if they do all work. It does not prove it
will work for others.

8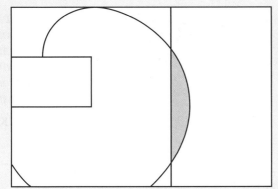

a   Straight line 5 cm from rail   *1 mark*
b   (Part) circle radius 5 cm   *1 mark*
     Quarter circle radius 2.5 cm   *1 mark*
c   Segment shaded blue   *1 mark*

TOTAL 4 MARKS

 Ruler, compasses and sharp pencil are needed to answer this question. Don't
obliterate your drawing with the shading.

9 a $3x - 6 + 8x - 12$ *1 mark*
            $= 11x - 18$ *1 mark*
b $10x^2 - 15x$ *1 mark*
c $2x^2 + 5x - 3x^2 + 6x$ *1 mark*
          $= -x^2 + 11x$ *1 mark*

TOTAL 5 MARKS

Be very careful with the negative signs.

10

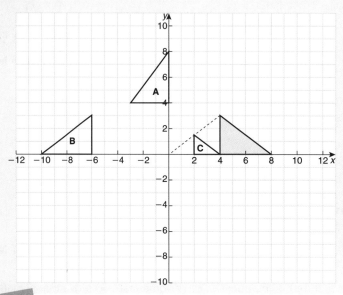

Two marks for each correct action: 6 marks
TOTAL 6 MARKS

There are two marks for each part. Any error will lose one mark.

11 a   100   *1 mark*
b (i)   785 hours   *1 mark*
  (ii) $880 - 600$ *1 mark*
            280 hours   *1 mark*
  (iii) $100 - 78 = 22$ *1 mark*
c   B, it has a longer average life (median 900 hours)   *1 mark*

TOTAL 6 MARKS

Even if you read one of the quartiles wrongly, you could get a mark for subtracting them. When giving your reason in part **c**, it is a good idea to include a statistic (in this case the median) to support what you say.

12 a $(x + 8)^2 = x^2 + (x + 7)^2$ *1 mark*
b $x^2 - 2x$ *1 mark*
          $-15 = 0$ *1 mark*
c $(x - 5)(x + 3) = 0$ *1 mark*
          $x = 5$ or $x = -3$ *1 mark*

TOTAL 5 MARKS

The solution of the equation gives two values for x, both of which you should have given. However, had you been asked to find the lengths of the sides of the triangle, $x = -3$ is not a possible value, so $x = 5$ gives the lengths 5, 12, 13.

13	ED = FB (opposite sides of a parallelogram)	*1 mark*
	FB = FA (given)	
	Angle AEF = Angle ECD	
	(corresponding angles, FE parallel to BC)	*1 mark*
	Angle DEC = Angle BAC	
	(corresponding angles DE parallel to BA)	*1 mark*
	Triangles congruent (AAS)	*1 mark*

TOTAL 4 MARKS

Examiner's tip

For this test of congruence to work, the equal sides must correspond, i.e. they must both be opposite equal angles.

TEST TOTAL 60 MARKS

Mental Mathematics Test: Answers

Mental Mathematics Test 1: Page 59

1	19	**9**	30 cm	**17**	78°	**25**	£4000
2	56	**10**	$x = 8$	**18**	16	**26**	2
3	2500	**11**	2.5	**19**	32	**27**	25%
4	10 000	**12**	0.04	**20**	30 kg	**28**	12
5	75	**13**	20	**21**	25	**29**	70.3
6	18	**14**	$\frac{1}{8}$ or 0.125	**22**	120	**30**	$\frac{85}{100}$ or $\frac{17}{20}$
7	15	**15**	4300	**23**	$\frac{11}{15}$		
8	600	**16**	$x = 1$ or 0	**24**	18		

Mental Mathematics Test 2: Page 60

1	4	**10**	7	**18**	e.g. −11, −20, −10.1	**25**	87°
2	1.8	**11**	−1			**26**	$\frac{6}{150}$ or $\frac{1}{25}$
3	750	**12**	$\frac{1}{100}$	**19**	Between 2 and 3 cm	**27**	17
4	9	**13**	9			**28**	0.0243 89
5	210	**14**	0.95	**20**	20%	**29**	22.5 s
6	6.5	**15**	45	**21**	6 cm²	**30**	Perpendicular bisector of line joining buoys
7	3.02	**16**	7 minutes 30 seconds	**22**	8		
8	12			**23**	249		
9	$2x$ hours	**17**	$\frac{1}{6}$	**24**	10 m		

Examiner's tip

You must listen carefully. 'Sixty' can sound like 'sixteen' if you are not concentrating. Ten seconds may not sound very long but, with practice, you should be able to answer questions like this in that time in your head. To get some more practice, ask someone to make up other questions like these, but with different numbers. Your score should soon improve – your target is to get them all right!

Determining your level

When you have marked a test, enter the total number of marks you scored for each question on the Marking grid overleaf. Then add them up and enter the test total on the grid.

Using the total for each test, look at the charts below to determine your level for each test.

Test A or Test B

Level 3 or below	Level 4	Level 5	Level 6
up to 13	14–26	27–39	40+

After you have worked out separate levels for Tests A and B and Mental Mathematics Test 1, add up your total marks for the three tests. Use this total and the chart below to determine your overall level for Maths at this point.

Total for Tests A and B and Mental Mathematics Test 1

Level 3 or below	Level 4	Level 5	Level 6
up to 31	32–63	64–94	95+

If your results from Tests A and B indicate that you are working at Level 4 or higher, you should try Tests C and D some time later. The chart below shows you how to find your level for each of Tests C and D.

Test C or Test D

Level 4 or below	Level 5	Level 6	Level 7 or above
up to 15	16–24	25–42	43+

If your results from Test C and D indicate that you are working at Level 6 or higher, you should try Test E. The chart below shows you how to find your level for Test E.

Test E

Level 5 or below	Level 6	Level 7	Level 8	Gifted & Talented
up to 13	14–24	25–41	42–50	51+

FINDING YOUR OVERALL LEVEL IN MATHS

After you have found your level for each test, add up your total marks for Tests C and D and Mental Mathematics Test 2. Use this total and the chart below to determine your overall level in Maths. The chart also shows you how your level compares with the target level for your age group.

Total for Tests C and D and Mental Mathematics Test 2

Level 4 or below	Level 5	Level 6	Level 7
up to 37	38–64	65–99	100+
Working towards target level	Working at target level for age group		Working beyond target level

Marking grid

Test A Pages 12–21

Question	Marks available	Marks scored	Question	Marks available	Marks scored	Question	Marks available	Marks scored
1	3		6	8		11	2	
2	4		7	4		12	6	
3	4		8	2		13	3	
4	2		9	4		14	4	
5	3		10	7		15	4	
						Total	**60**	

Test B Pages 22–31

Question	Marks available	Marks scored	Question	Marks available	Marks scored	Question	Marks available	Marks scored
1	4		5	6		9	4	
2	6		6	5		10	5	
3	8		7	5		11	6	
4	5		8	2		12	4	
						Total	**60**	

Test C Pages 32–39

Question	Marks available	Marks scored	Question	Marks available	Marks scored	Question	Marks available	Marks scored
1	5		5	5		9	6	
2	2		6	5		10	3	
3	4		7	6		11	5	
4	7		8	7		12	5	
						Total	**60**	

Test D Pages 40–48

Question	Marks available	Marks scored	Question	Marks available	Marks scored	Question	Marks available	Marks scored
1	4		5	4		9	5	
2	7		6	4		10	7	
3	3		7	4		11	3	
4	10		8	2		12	7	
						Total	**60**	

Test E Pages 49–56

Question	Marks available	Marks scored	Question	Marks available	Marks scored	Question	Marks available	Marks scored
1	4		6	5		11	6	
2	3		7	4		12	5	
3	2		8	4		13	4	
4	6		9	5				
5	6		10	6		**Total**	**60**	

	Marks available	Marks scored
Mental Mathematics Test 1 (p. 59)	30	
Mental Mathematics Test 2 (p. 60)	30	

Also available from *Letts*

More essential reading from the brand leaders in home study

Achieve SATs success with our Key Stage 3 Success Guides available in Maths, English and Science.

> **Brightly coloured and easy to use revision guides**
>
> **RRP: £3.99**

The ultimate Maths and English course companions for Key Stage 3.
One book available for each year 7, 8 and 9.

> **The ultimate Maths and English guides for Key Stage 3**
>
> **RRP: £4.99**

Available at all good bookshops, or visit www.letts-education.com

To register and receive your free book simply log on to:

   www.letts-education.com†

✉   or send your details‡ (Name, Age, School year,
Address, Postcode, Email) to:
Free Book Offer, Letts Educational,
414 Chiswick High Road, London W4 5TF

† For e-mail registration: postage and packing payable as detailed on the website.

‡ For postal registration: in order to receive your free book, please send
a self-addressed envelope with stamps to the value of £1.

Letts Educational reserve the right to close this promotion without prior notification.
No purchase necessary.

FREE BOOK *worth £3.50 or more when you register on our website today*